GRANDREAMS proudly welcomes

THE OFFICIAL

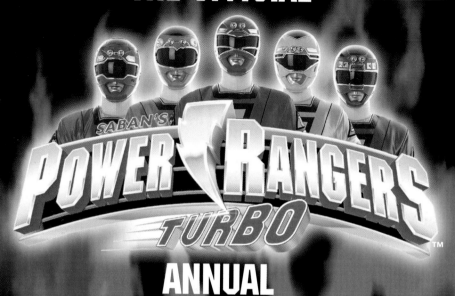

SABAN'S

POWER RANGERS
TURBO™
ANNUAL

The legendary Power Rangers – now known as **POWER RANGERS TURBO** – feature in the fifth season of TV's smash-hit children's action adventure series. And they now boast some brand new powers and some brand new Zords!

These are the Turbo Zords – five off-road and out-of-this-world vehicles which provide the Power Rangers with the awesome velocity needed to defend the Earth from on-going alien assault. Each vehicle reflects the personality of the Turbo Ranger who drives it.

The five Power Teens use their awesome new gifts in their endless fight against evil – and against such malevolent monstrosities as the awful Divatox and her motley crew of minions.

This Official Annual takes a look at the Turbo Power Rangers, their amazing Turbo Zords, their new allies – and, of course, their evil enemies.

SO...GET REVVED-UP AND LET'S
HIT THE ROAD TO TURBO FUN!!!

£5.99

POWER RANGERS TURBO WARNING!

Each member of the *Power Rangers Turbo* cast has been specially trained in the disciplines of martial arts. Never, ever attempt to recreate any of their routines, tricks or stunts – and never, ever use kicks on your friends!

POWER RANGERS TURBO WARNING!

Edited by Tony Lynch
Designed by Jason Bazini

Published by Grandreams Ltd
435-437 Edgware Road
Little Venice
London W2 1TH

Printed in Belgium

CONTENTS

THE WEIRD AND WONDERFUL SAGA OF THE POWER RANGERS

THE FASCINATING STORY OF THE POWER RANGERS BEGAN MANY AEONS AGO IN A SOLAR SYSTEM FAR, FAR AWAY. IT WAS BORN OUT OF A BATTLE BETWEEN THE POWERS OF GOOD AND THE POWERS OF EVIL...

On the side of good was Zordon: wizard, sage, scholar and a true champion of all that is honest, just and true in the universe. He knew that without the overwhelming influence of good, our lives would be pointless and we would

terrible fighting, the fate of the universe was to be decided on the flip of a coin – a simple game of heads or tails!

The coin was tossed – and Zordon won. Rita was none too pleased and insisted they go for 'the best of five'.

And still she lost. Zordon now held the future of Rita Repulsa, and her repugnant followers, in the palm of his hand. Zordon decided not to eliminate Rita and her motley crew, in spite of all the bad things they had done. Instead, he imprisoned them inside a sealed Zithium Cylinder (a kind of outer space rubbish bin). Then he cast them adrift among the galaxies,

all be lost to the putrid powers of evil.

The opposite point of view was held by Zordon's arch enemy, Rita Repulsa, the Empress of Evil. Rita was not only bad to the bone, she was ambitious too – she wanted to rule all the galaxies in the known universe and didn't care what evil deeds she had to perform to achieve that ambition.

The war lasted for more than 2,000 years. The battles raged across countless time lines and in many of the parallel universes that exist in the vastness of space.

Eventually – after several innocent planets, moons and stars were destroyed in the conflict – the wise Zordon decided that the war must end. He proposed a simple solution and, believe it or not, Rita Repulsa agreed to it. And so, after all that

the 'black holes' and all the other mysterious elements that make up the known universe.

With Rita and her cronies gone forever, intergalactic space was declared safe once again.

The Zithium Cylinder drifted around for a thousand years and covered over a gazillion space miles. In all that time, Rita was not idle. She devised an extremely cunning plan, and trapped Zordon in an inter-dimensional time warp.

Then the cylinder landed with a bump, on the small lump of round rock that orbits planet Earth, our very own Moon. There it stayed, still sealed,

THE WEIRD AND WONDERFUL SAGA
OF THE POWER RANGERS

still safe, for many more years – until the clever scientists and space boffins on Earth eventually succeeded in sending astronauts to the Moon. It was two of these guys who one day stumbled upon the weird-looking cylinder.

Rita managed to trick the astronauts into releasing her, and once again her ghastly ambitions were unleashed upon the Earth. She blew up mountain ranges, sucked entire lakes dry, demanded blind obedience of all Earthlings and generally ticked everyone off.

Zordon had actually anticipated that Rita might one day escape from her cylindrical jail. And, to counter this awful happening, he had secreted an Inter-dimensional Communicator and a super powered computer in a Command Centre somewhere in the California Desert.

The Command Centre was controlled by a specially trained android called Alpha 5. It was he who first detected Rita's presence on Earth.

Alpha relayed this information to Zordon (who remained in the time warp and appeared only through an Energy Tube built into the Command Centre). Zordon instantly ordered Alpha to seek out the very best means of combating Rita's new threat

to the safety of planet Earth.

Using the Inter-dimensional Communicator, Alpha conducted some serious research. He eventually deduced that the two most powerful forces so far known to Man were Pre-historic Dinosaurs and Teenagers with Attitude!!!

Zordon took Alpha 5's findings on board and then – using the Inter-dimensional Communicator – set about collecting some fossilised dinosaur remains from Earth. He extracted the essence of these ancient bones and used it to give power and dynamism to five Dino Zords – Pterodactyl, Triceratops, Tyrannosaurus Rex, Mastodon and Sabre-Toothed Tiger. These Dino Zords were exactly like the ancient animals except for the addition of guidance and weapons systems, super propulsion, bucket seats, air-conditioning and anti-lock brakes!

The next task assigned to Alpha 5 was to recruit five 'teenagers with attitude', each with special personality traits and physical skills. These recruits would man the Dino Zords and help combat the threat posed by Rita Repulsa.

The quest was eventually narrowed down to five extra special youngsters – all from the town of Angel Grove where they were students at the High School. Under Zordon's direction Jason became the Red Ranger; Trini was appointed the Yellow Ranger; Billy was the Blue Ranger; Zack became the Black Ranger and Kimberly took on the role of the Pink Ranger.

Each of these Power Teens then took possession of a Dino Zord, a Power Coin and a personal weapon, created to enhance their own physical capabilities.

The identity of this fighting force was kept top secret. In everyday life they were simply five bright young students – but when called into action they would *morph* into their Power Ranger personas.

Now Zordon was ready to launch a counter-attack on Rita Repulsa. And the Empress of Evil was about to meet the most powerful force in all the galaxies...*The Mighty Morphin Power Rangers*.

It was an awesome responsibility for the Power Teens as they adjusted to the impact that the new powers and weapons had on their lives. But they handled it all with great poise.

They discovered different ways to combine their Dino Zords to create different levels of firepower, even bringing all five together to form the almost invincible Megazord.

They scored some early successes against the Evil Empress and her creepy cronies. And Rita grew increasingly annoyed and frustrated that the Power Teens were spoiling her plans and thwarting her awful ambitions.

Then Rita came up with a devilish plan. Using an ancient Power Coin, she transformed a local lad called Tommy into the Green Ranger – her own personal Power Ranger. She infiltrated Tommy into the Teens' trust, intending to use him against them.

But there was a fatal flaw in Rita's plan. Tommy was basically a good person. He fought with all his might against her influence. And, with Jason's help, Tommy eventually freed himself from Rita's spell.

Rita Repulsa was absolutely livid at this turn of events and she became even more determined to destroy the Power Rangers – especially Tommy!

Rita did all kinds of nasty things including: kidnapping the Power Rangers' parents...creating evil replicas of the Power Rangers...and feeding them substances that turned them from good to evil. But somehow the Power

THE WEIRD AND WONDERFUL SAGA
OF THE POWER RANGERS

Rangers always managed to get the better of her.

Rita's boss, Lord Zedd, had watched all of her efforts in dealing with the Power Rangers. He thought she was rather pathetic, and felt that he could do a much better job himself.

Lord Zedd was a towering, well-muscled creature with a blood-red exterior and razor-sharp body armour. At his disposal was an entire army of monsters. These monstrosities had been created with Zedd's own personal touch and inspired by Earthly plants and animals. They included Robogot, Octophantom, the Invenusable Fly Trap, Guitardo and Pachinko Head.

With a power more awesome than anything the Rangers had ever encountered before, Lord Zedd destroyed the Dino Zords. But even he had not expected to come up against the ingenuity of Alpha 5. Using fragments of the broken Dinozords, the clever little android was able to reconstruct them as the Thunder Zords, called Unicorn, Tiger, Dragon, Lion, Griffin and Firebird.

Around this time Jason, Trini and Zack were selected to attend the World Peace Conference in Switzerland. With their strength cut in half, the remaining Power Rangers were saved from certain defeat, thanks to the wisdom of their mentor, Zordon.

Zordon selected three new teens whose high moral character and superior strength and fortitude made them ideal candidates to join the ranks of the Power Rangers. And so the powers of the three departing Rangers were transferred to Rocky who became the Red Power Ranger; Aisha who took on the mantle of the Yellow Power Ranger; and Adam who became the Black Power Ranger.

Zordon then strengthened the power squad by recalling Tommy to the fold, as the White Ranger. Once again they were ready to take on any evil force in the universe.

Meanwhile, Rita Repulsa and Lord Zedd also strengthened their union – when Rita tricked Zedd into marriage.

While apart they had caused more than enough mayhem, but together they spelled double-trouble, especially when they formed a horrendous and dangerous new army of monstrous beings, all willing to help in the cause of universal domination.

Rita and Zedd eventually succeeded in destroying the Thunder Zords – and it looked for all the world as if the Power Rangers were defeated.

But Zordon told the Teens about the Temple of Power, and Ninjor, the Keeper of the Temple. It was he who had forged the original Power Coins.

The Teens set out to find Ninjor, and to receive new powers. Their search took them across the Desert of Despair, where they were set upon by Tenga Warriors sent by Rita and Zedd.

The Power Rangers escaped this ambush, and eventually arrived at the Temple of Power. There, Ninjor endowed them with brand new powers and new Zords. Called Ninjazords, these incredible machines drew their powers from the Falcon, the Crane, the Ape, the Shark, the Wolf and the Bear.

Once again the Power Rangers were ready to protect the Earth from the likes of the evil Lord Zedd and his unlovely wife Rita Repulsa.

The Power Rangers made a new friend, Katherine. Unfortunately she was under Rita's powerful spell and she captured the Falconzord. This rendered the other Ninjazords inoperable. But when Katherine had a vision of her childhood, she realised that she was not evil at all and was able to break free of Rita forever.

Katherine eventually took over from Kimberly, as the Pink Ranger. And she was put to work immediately when Rita's father, Master Vile – unable to stand the incompetence of his daughter and her husband any longer – arrived on Earth determined to put an end to the Power Rangers once and for all.

Master Vile set out to capture and utilise the Zeo Crystal, a supremely powerful gem that was guarded by a force field.

The Power Rangers decided to locate the Crystal and destroy it before its powers could be used for evil.

The Teens succeeded in finding the gem which they dismantled before scattering its pieces around the world. Then Master Vile unleashed his ultimate plan: he turned the Earth back in time. This reduced the Power Rangers to powerless children who could only look on helplessly as Zedd, Rita and their nasty cronies wreaked havoc on Angel Grove.

The child Rangers eventually recovered and reassembled the Zeo Crystal in the Command Centre.

Zedd and Rita launched a massive attack on the Command Centre which erupted in an explosion and was reduced to a pile of smoking debris. It seemed that Zordon and Alpha 5 had been destroyed too, and that the evil beings had probably stolen the Zeo Crystal at last.

But the Teens began digging in the burnt and blackened soil where the Command Centre had once stood – and they

THE WEIRD AND WONDERFUL SAGA OF THE POWER RANGERS

unearthed the Zeo Crystal. It had survived the attack, and still worked its magic!

As Tommy held the Crystal in his hands, it began to glow. Its light filled the air, and the ground began to rumble and shake. The Teens found themselves falling through space and they landed in what used to be the Command Centre basement.

To their great surprise they discovered Alpha 5 there, still intact. He told them to step into the Vortex, a beautiful multi-coloured force field, beyond which was a room that none of them had ever seen before.

This was the Power Chamber. Alpha 5 explained that it had been there since the beginning, as Zordon knew that the Command Centre would one day come under attack.

Thanks to the magical powers of the Zeo Crystal, the Command Centre re-assembled itself. Then Zordon appeared in the Energy Tube and informed the Teens that Rita and Lord Zedd had fled to the far reaches of the universe. But now a new force of evil – the Machine Empire – had invaded our galaxy.

The Machine Empire was ruled by King Mondo and Queen Machina who commanded an army of Cogs, mechanised fighting robots that did not know the meaning of surrender.

But how on Earth were the Power Rangers going to combat this new force?

Zordon explained that even though the Power Coins were gone forever, there was a new energy source at the Rangers' disposal. It came from Zeo Crystal, and it gave the Rangers greater powers than ever before – this was Zeo Power.

Zordon issued each Ranger with a Zeonizer, which allowed them to morph and to call upon their new Zeo powers.

Billy relinquished his position as the Blue Ranger. Then Zordon bestowed each Ranger with their Zeo powers: Tommy, the leader, became the Red Zeo Ranger; Katherine retained the Pink assignment; Rocky became the Blue Zeo Ranger; Adam donned the Green uniform and Tanya joined the team as the new Yellow Zeo Ranger in place of Aisha...and they were ready to take on whatever Mondo and Machina could throw at them.

The twisted royals, aided by an entire arsenal of machine-monsters, certainly gave the young heroes a terrible time.

The Zeo Power Rangers were helped in their struggle by the arrival of the mysterious and ultra-powerful Gold Ranger. This was Trey, Lord of the distant planet Triforia. He came from a race of peace keepers and roamed the galaxy helping those in need.

After helping the Power Rangers battle Rita and Zedd, Trey returned to Triforia to be replaced as the Gold Ranger by Jason, who returned from a peace conference to accept the new power.

Just when all seemed calm again, Rita and Zedd returned to do battle with Mondo and Machina, all of them desiring to rule the universe.

The Zeo Rangers managed to thwart the evil plans of the dual foe. Then, in a surprise move, Lord Zedd attempted to make peace with Mondo and Machina. He gave them a present, which turned out to be a bomb. Mondo and Machina were blown away.

Meanwhile, Jason's powers began to fade mysteriously, and Billy left Angel Grove for a new life on another world.

The remaining Zeo Power Rangers were left wondering what new challenges would face them.

The answer appeared in the shape of Divatox. This barbaric lady pirate was intent on unleashing the greatest evil ever known to man – the beast known as Maligore.

First Divatox had to capture Lerigot, a kindly wizard from the planet Liaria. Lerigot held the only golden key capable of releasing Maligore from his volcanic prison on the island of Muranthis.

The Power Rangers were called upon to help and protect the little wizard.

Divatox used all the wicked resources at her command to ensure that her plan of uniting with Maligore was brought to fruition.

The Power Teens faced many perilous situations in Africa and at the bottom of the ocean, where they battled Divatox's warriors, the Piranathons.

Everything came to a head at the volcano on Muranthis. And it was then that the wise Zordon realised that he had to bestow new powers upon the Rangers if they were to stand any chance of winning this particular confrontation.

These were the Turbo powers...and they destroyed Maligore, defeated Divatox and ruined her plans to dominate the universe.

Zordon was at last released from his inter-dimensional time warp and returned to his home planet taking his trusted servant Alpha 5 with him.

Without these two powerful allies the Turbo Power Rangers remained in jeopardy – until the arrival of Zordon's beautiful replacement, Dimitria, who provides the wisdom and direction the Rangers need to take on Divatox.

As always, there are plenty of new surprises in store...especially as Divatox will do anything and everything to get her revenge on the Turbo Power Rangers...

THE RED TURBO

TOMMY

Tommy has had a pretty weird life as a Power Ranger. First he was the Green Ranger planted amid the Power Teens by wicked Rita Repulsa in her attempt to destroy them.

Thankfully, Tommy eventually broke free of Rita's evil influence, and Zordon was so impressed with him that he appointed him leader of the Power Rangers and gave him the White assignment. When the *Mighty Morphin Power Rangers* became the *Zeo Power Rangers*, Tommy was reassigned to the Red uniform.

In *Power Rangers Turbo*, Tommy takes on a summer job building a racing car with the enthusiastic and very clever Justin as his helpful assistant.

Tommy is brave, heroic and responsible and has a powerful sense of duty. He also has a great sense of humour and enjoys martial arts and other sports.

There is a romantic relationship between Tommy and the Pink Power Ranger, Kat.

RANGER FILE

TOMMY, PORTRAYED BY
JASON DAVID FRANK

THE RED RANGER'S VEHICLES

RED LIGHTNING TURBO ZORD

RED RACER

THE RED TURBO RANGER FILE

T.J.

T.J. arrived in Angel Grove on board a bus, on which he first met Cassie, who was destined to become the Pink Turbo Ranger. The two teens did not realise it, but they were about to make quite an entrance into the little town!

They quickly saw that Tommy and Kat were in big trouble and they did not hesitate to help them.

When the Power Rangers decided to hand their powers on, T.J became the new Red Ranger, and took on the mantle of leadership.

He is a seventeen-year-old African-American. He is athletic, intelligent and a born leader. He leads by example, not by force, and his gentle nature and charming smile seem to draw people to him.

T.J. is the cool, calm balance to Carlos' hot-blooded character. The new Red leader is always assessing the situation, making sure that everyone is working together – he is a worthy successor to Tommy.

POWER RANGERS TURBO

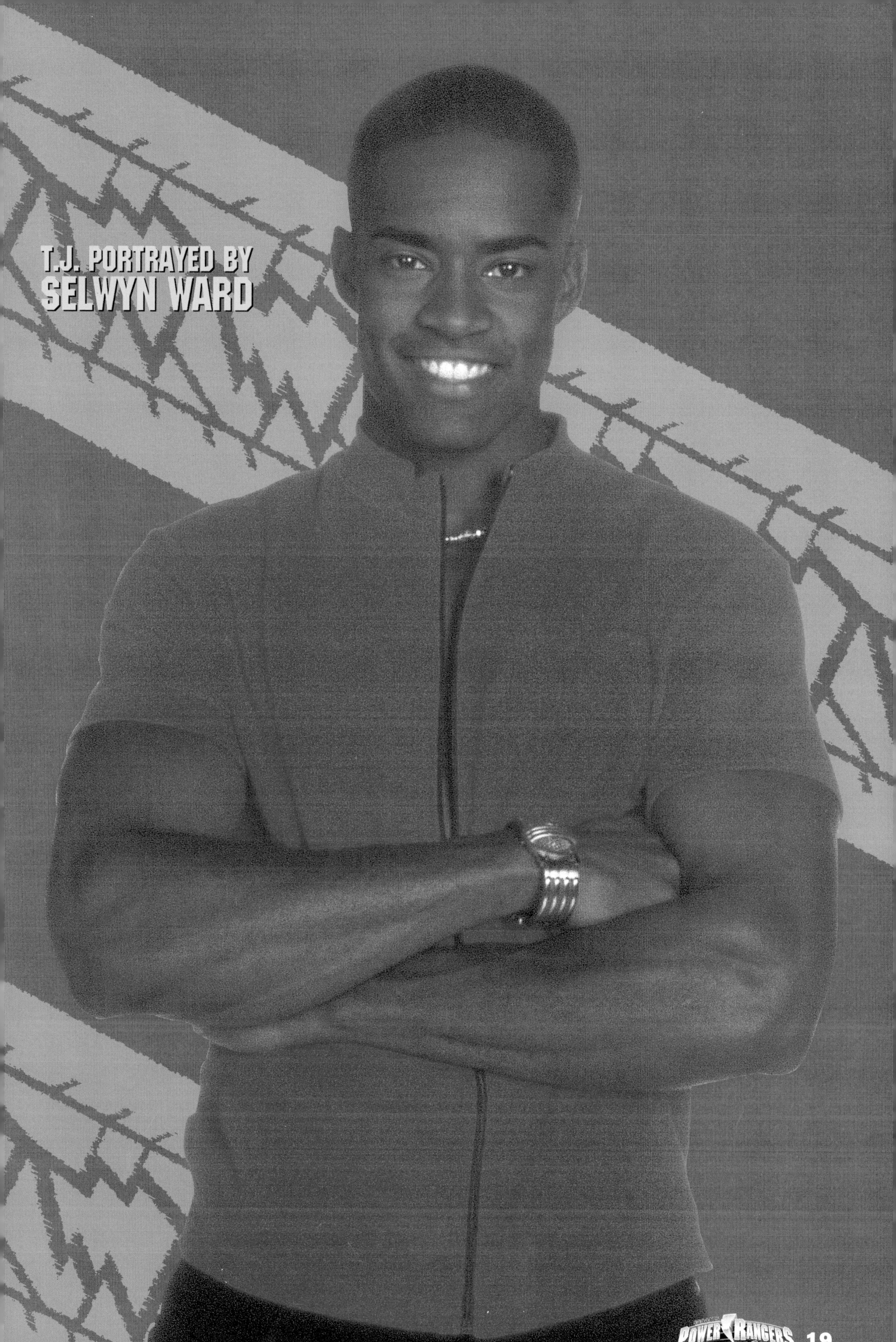
T.J. PORTRAYED BY
SELWYN WARD

LOOK OUT — IT'S DIVATOX!

Divatox looked down upon a sea of warriors and monsters... hundreds of them. They all stared up at her in adulation and were chanting her name.

'Silence,' she cried – and the crowd instantly obeyed the command. 'Warriors, monsters, faithful followers,' she continued. 'You are all aware of the reason we are here.'

A cheer rose from the crowd – and they began chanting: 'Destroy them! Destroy them!'

Divatox spoke again: 'The ruination of my plan to dominate the universe must be avenged. The Power Rangers will pay dearly. Their beloved Earth will become mine. Are you with me?!!!!'

And the crowd erupted again, cheering wildly.

From this evil scene you can see the power that Divatox wields over her many minions. And you can see just what a task the Turbo Rangers face.

A one-woman wrecking crew, Divatox is an arch-villain intent on destroying the Power Rangers. The only things that really matter to this barbaric pirate of the cosmos are fame, fortune and her own diminishing beauty.

A lifetime of evil has turned her into a vain, bitter, fortune-hunting shrew with an acerbic wit to cut down anyone who crosses her.

Under her vicious and dominating rule, Divatox's minions cower at the very mention of her name.

In her powerful vessel, the Subcraft, she works day and night to achieve her ultimate goal – to destroy or enslave the Turbo Power Rangers.

THE BLUE TURBO

ROCKY, PORTRAYED BY
STEVE CARDENAS

RANGER FILE

ROCKY

After taking over from the original Red Ranger, Jason, Rocky De Santos gave sterling service as a member of the Power Teens as they battled the forces of evil.

He is a charismatic teen with an easy-going nature and a ready smile playing on his lips.

When Zordon bestowed the Zeo powers on the Power Teens, Rocky became the Blue Ranger.

When his parents broke up he was left to help his mother bring up the family's six younger children. The De Santoses lived in a poor neighbourhood

and there were endless chores for Rocky to attend to.

It was to get away from the pressures of his domestic life, that he first began to train in the martial arts.

With constant practice he quickly gained grade after grade, and finally found himself the proud possessor of a Black Belt.

And, of course, those martial arts skills were vital to Rocky's secret life as a Power Ranger.

After receiving a nasty injury in a karate accident, Rocky passed the Blue Ranger assignment on to young Justin.

THE BLUE RANGER'S VEHICLES

SIREN BLASTER TURBO ZORD

BLUE TURBO CART

THE BLUE TURBO RANGER FILE

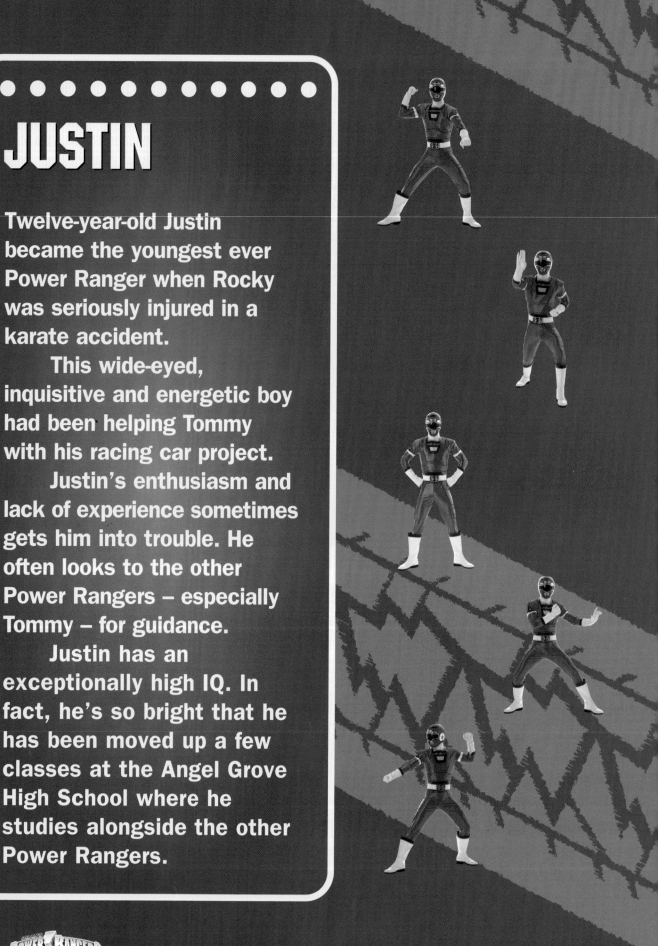

JUSTIN

Twelve-year-old Justin became the youngest ever Power Ranger when Rocky was seriously injured in a karate accident.

This wide-eyed, inquisitive and energetic boy had been helping Tommy with his racing car project.

Justin's enthusiasm and lack of experience sometimes gets him into trouble. He often looks to the other Power Rangers – especially Tommy – for guidance.

Justin has an exceptionally high IQ. In fact, he's so bright that he has been moved up a few classes at the Angel Grove High School where he studies alongside the other Power Rangers.

Power Rangers TURBO™

JUSTIN PORTRAYED BY
BLAKE FOSTER

THE EVIL-

RYGOG

Rygog is second-in-command to Divatox, and will do anything and destroy anyone for his evil mistress.

His exceptionally vile disposition and menacing appearance ignite fear in the hearts of all who encounter him.

He barks orders fiercely to his underlings, but he becomes nothing more than a boot-licking toady when it comes to Divatox. In fact, he is always crawling around her.

Although Divatox always trusts Rygog to carry out her evil deeds, she treats him with utter contempt and disdain whenever he attempts to suck up to her.

He really is such a creep!

DOERS FILE

ELGAR

Elgar is Divatox's tall, turnip-brained nephew. He is constantly on hand with some bonehead comment – or some ridiculous observation on the obvious.

He constantly botches his aunt's vile schemes – and whenever that happens she is quick to go all Medieval and unleash her wrath upon him.

Elgar is more of a liability than an asset to Divatox's plans. But, then again, he is family!

PORTO

Porto is the snivelling henchman who serves as the brains behind Divatox's nautical operations. He is also the creator of the monsters used in her endless quest for power.

With a creepy voice and manner, Porto is in charge of all things to do with the remarkable Subcraft – which he designed and built.

Most of the time, Porto is filled with resentment at being nothing more than the Subcraft's Technical Officer. Despite his superior intellect, he remains reduced to taking orders from Divatox and Rygog and taking them wherever they want to go.

Porto is always complaining and insulting his masters under his breath.

THE PIRANHATRONS

These warriors are the evil foot-soldiers deployed by Divatox and her crew – to divert the Turbo Power Rangers at every opportunity.

Although less fantastic than the monsters which Porto creates for Divatox, the Piranhatrons are no less dangerous.

More often than not, these warriors strike unannounced – often challenging the Turbo Power Rangers in their civilian, or un-morphed state.

CAUTION
NO LIFT TRUCKS
ALLOWED BEYOND
THIS POINT

THE GREEN TURBO

ADAM, PORTRAYED BY
JOHNNY YONG BOSCH

POWER RANGERS
TURBO

RANGER FILE

ADAM

Handsome young Korean-American Adam Park is spiritual and shy, with a subtle sense of humour that makes him both funny and charming.

In the summer Adam discovered a new interest when he became involved with the Angel Grove Stunt Show. There he is able to showcase his physical talents by playing different roles in the show, and each time he wows the audience!

He also shares a special friendship with Yellow Turbo Power Ranger, Tanya.

Adam was once the Black Power Ranger, but Zordon reassigned him to the Green uniform when distributing the Zeo powers.

When he was much younger he used to get pushed around at school. That's when he turned to studying martial arts – and being a very fast learner, he discovered he had a brand new talent – and quickly found that he wasn't bullied anymore!

THE GREEN RANGER'S
VEHICLES

DESERT THUNDER
TURBO ZORD

GREEN TURBO CART

THE GREEN TURBO RANGER FILE

CARLOS

Carlos is a good-looking, very athletic seventeen-year-old Mexican-American. He's a good student, popular with the other kids, and is the star of the Angel Grove soccer team.

What's more, he is every young girl's dream date!

Carlos can be headstrong at times and has a strong sense of justice, always seeing an issue as either black or white.

CARLOS, PORTRAYED BY
ROGER VELASCO

POWER RANGERS TURBO ™ 37

BLUE SENTURION

The Blue Senturion came to present-day Earth from the future and doesn't know or understand the happenings of everyday life in the 20th Century. The Turbo Power Rangers regard him as their protector. Yet they also look out for him, as he is kind of naive and not altogether with it in the present day.

"SENTURION CYCLE, INITIATE ONLINE COMMAND!"

"ROBO RACER, INITIATE ONLINE COMMAND!"

"SYNERGISER, BLASTER MODE"

"SYNERGISER, BLADE MODE"

THE PHANTOM RANGER

This mysterious character embodies the spiritual essence of all Power Rangers, past and present. He arrives and departs in a strange apparition. He is part real, part ghost and never discloses his identity. The Phantom Ranger gives the Power Rangers an awesome new fleet of Zords – the Rescue Zords – along with the Artillatron, the Turbo transporter.

THE YELLOW TURBO

TANYA

Tanya loves music and would just love to become a famous pop star. She also loves to read, and really enjoys all kinds of sporting activities.

She has a very dry sense of humour and a wry wit.

Since she used to live in Africa, Tanya is very interested in African culture and tradition.

She works on her martial arts skills with her friend and co-Ranger Adam. Tanya works at the local Angel Grove radio station so she can learn as much as she possibly can about the recording industry.

Power Rangers TURBO ™

RANGER FILE

TANYA, PORTRAYED BY
NAKIA BURRISE

THE YELLOW RANGER'S VEHICLES

DUNE STAR TURBO ZORD

YELLOW TURBO CART

ASHLEY

Ashley is a bubbly, positive, upbeat person who always sees the bright side of a situation. She is a cheerleader who is popular with the other kids, and belongs to just about every club at Angel Grove High School.

There are times when her grades suffer, due to her over-involvement in school activities, but she always manages to pull through.

Ashley's dream is to one day become a top fashion designer – the next Donna Karan, perhaps!

ASHLEY, PORTRAYED BY
TRACY LYNN CRUZ

ALPHA 6

POWER RANGERS
TURBO ™

ALPHA 6

Alpha 6 replaced Alpha 5 when the older android returned to his home planet with Zordon.

Alpha 6 is quite different from his predecessor. He raises a lot of laughs with his brash, street-smart personality.

DIMITRIA

Dimitria, a beautiful sorceress, is a champion of good in the universe – just like Zordon.

She came to the aid of the Power Rangers in a time of great need. When Zordon and Alpha 5 returned to their home dimension, the world was left defenceless and was attacked by Dimitria's evil twin sister, Divatox!

Dimitria knows that she must help the Turbo Power Rangers to protect the Earth from her sister's wrath. She appears to them as a three-dimensional holograph in the Power Chamber. She is a sage and mentor to the Power Teens, although sometimes her advice can be just a little cryptic.

THE PINK TURBO

Power Rangers Turbo ™

RANGER FILE

KAT

Kat, a native of Australia, is a born leader who is interested in helping her community and caring for the environment. Her training in dance gives her a graceful and elegant style. In the summer Kat became a student teacher at Justin's summer school – and discovered that he is a child genius!

THE PINK RANGER'S VEHICLES

PINK TURBO CART

WIND CHASER TURBO ZORD

THE PINK TURBO RANGER FILE

CASSIE

Cassie, a seventeen-year-old Asian-American, is a bit of a rebel. Her taste in clothes leans towards a slightly grunge-rocker style – and she would love to play guitar in an all-girl rock band!

Cassie is strong-willed, independent – and she has a softer side with an iron resolve that will take her far in life. Her dream is to one day become a champion martial artist.

POWER RANGERS TURBO™

CASSIE, PORTRAYED BY
PATRICIA JA LEE

Power Rangers TURBO ™ 53

THE

TURBO MEGAZORD

THE TURBO MEGAZORD IS AN AWESOME

COMBINATION OF THE FIVE ZORDS...

- Red Lightning
- Dune Star
- Wind Chaser
- Desert Thunder
- Mountain Blaster

RESCUE MEGAZORD

FIVE POWERFUL VEHICLES...

- Lightning Fire Tamer
- Siren Blaster
- Thunder Loader
- Star Racer
- Wind Rescue

...PUT TOGETHER TO MAKE ONE INCREDIBLE MEGAZORD!

MEGAZORDS

ARTILLATRON

Artillatron is the storage and transportation
Zord which dispatches the Rescue Zord. When
the Rescue Megazord is formed, it can get
extra artillery power from the Artillatron in the
form of a flaming cannon and a rotating laser.

DIVATOX'S

HERE ARE JUST SOME OF THE MALEVOLENT MONSTERS ENCOUNTERED

MONSTERS

BY THE POWER TEENS IN POWER RANGERS TURBO...

WELCOME TO THE PUZZLE ZONE

DIVATOX HAS SET SOME MIND-BOGGLING PUZZLES. SEE IF YOU CAN OUTWIT HER BY SOLVING THEM.

POWER RANGERS TURBO — WORD TREE

Can you fit the 17 POWER RANGERS TURBO words listed here into their correct places in the word tree?

ASHLEY
BLUE
CARLOS
CLOCKSTER
CROSSPATCH
DIMITRIA
DIVATOX
ELECTROVOLT
GREEN
GRILLER
JUSTIN
MEGAZORD
PHANTOM
PINK
RED
ROBO
YELLOW

```
              P L N K
        C L O R _ _ _ _ _ _
    _ _ _ _ _ _ W E R
        _ _ _ W E R
        _ _ R _ _ _ _ _ _ _ _
            R _ _
            A _ _ _ _
    _ _ _ N _ _ _ _
            G _ _ _ _
    _ _ G E R _ _ _ _ _ _ _
            R
            S
            _ _ _ _ _ T _ _
            _ U R B O
    _ _ _ _ _ T U R B O
        _ _ _ R B O
    _ _ _ _ _ O
```

SOLUTION ON PAGE 62

58

SPOT THE DIFFERENCES!

One of Divatox's minions has made **EIGHT** changes to the
POWER RANGERS TURBO picture at the bottom of the page. Can you find them all?

SOLUTION ON PAGE 62

WELCOME TO THE PUZZLE ZONE

POWER RANGERS TURBO WORDSEARCH

There are **21 POWER RANGERS TURBO** words hidden in the grid below. They may be hidden forwards, backwards, up, down or diagonally. Can you find them all?

ARTILLATRON
ASHLEY
CARLOS
CASSIE
CYCLE
DIVATOX
ELGAR
LIGHTNING
PHANTOM
PIRANHATRONS
PORTO
POWER
RANGERS
RESCUE
ROBO
SENTURION
SWORD
TERRORTOOTH
THUNDER
TURBO
ZORDS

SOLUTION ON PAGE 62

LERIGOT

Lerigot is a lovable wizard from the planet Liaria. He appears in the Power Chamber, returning in order to give Zordon his freedom to rejoin his own family.

PUZZLE SOLUTIONS

POWER RANGERS TURBO — WORDTREE
(PAGE 58)

SPOT THE DIFFERENCES
(PAGE 59)

```
        PINK
      CLOCKSTER
YELLOW
    BLUE
      CROSSPATCH

      RED
      ASHLEY
  PHANTOM
      GREEN
      ELECTROVOLT
  DIMITRIA
  CARLOS

    DIVATOX
      JUSTIN
  GRILLER
      ROBO
  MEGAZORD
```

WORDSEARCH
(PAGE 60)

```
R A N G E R S P Q R C T T
C R S P S D R O Z X A D E
Y T X H O D O W H G S T R
C I O A L D G E U C S E R
L L T N R E I R U E I Y O
E L A A A Y B F H E U R R
G A V O C T H U N D E R T
G T I M I O T P P R N B O
A R D X S B W Q P O R T O
R O B O M R U Y T W P P T
X N O I R U T N E S L J H
C G N I N T H G I L B C A
P I R A N H A T R O N S Q
```